Editor: Chad Beard ● **Cover Design:** Michele Winkelman ● **Design & Layout:** Cecil Anderson and Lynette Rowe
Special Thanks: Cheryl Brown Henderson *(President, Brown Foundation for Educational Equity, Excellence and Research)* and Martin Wisneski *(Head of Technical Services, Washburn University School of Law Library)*

Gallopade is proud to be a member of these educational organizations and associations:

The National School Supply and Equipment Association (NSSEA)
National Association for Gifted Children (NAGC)
American Booksellers Association (ABA)
Museum Store Association (MSA)
Publishers Marketing Association (PMA)
International Reading Association (IRA)
Supporter of **Association of Partners for Public Lands (APPL)**

Published by
GALLOPADE™
INTERNATIONAL
800-536-2GET
www.gallopade.com

CAROLE MARSH BOOKS

1

Other Carole Marsh Books

Orville & Wilbur Wright . . . Step Out Into The Sky!
Lewis & Clark Go On a Hike: The Story of the Corps of Discovery
"What A Deal!": The Louisiana Purchase
How Our Nation Was Born: The American Revolution
When Brother Fought Brother: The American Civil War
The Fight For Equality: The U.S. Civil Rights Movement
"It Can't Be Wrong!": The Bill of Rights
"Sign on the Dotted Line!": The U.S. Constitution
"Quit Bossing Us Around!": The Declaration of Independence

State Stuff™, Available for all 50 states:

My First Pocket Guide
State My First Book
State Wheel of Fortune Gamebook
State Survivor Gamebook
State Illustrated Timelines
"Jography!": A Fun Run Through Our State

The State Coloring Book
The Big Reproducible Activity Book
State Millionaire Gamebook
State Project Books
Jeopardy: Answers & Questions About
   Our State

Patriotic Favorites™

Patriotic Favorites Coloring Book
Patriotic Biographies
The Daily Patriot: 365 Quotations

Young Patriots Coloring & Activity Book
Patriotic Projects
Patriotisms: 365 Definitions

Table of Contents

A Word From the Author .... page 4

A Timeline of Events .... page 5

I Want To Go To School!: Brown v. Board of Education .... page 6

Equal Protection under the Law .... page 8

"Jim Crow" Laws .... page 9

Separate but Equal .... page 10

Niagara Movement and the NAACP .... page 11

Attention Class .... page 12

Building Blocks of *Brown* .... page 13

Segregation .... page 14

Who Was Brown? .... page 15

Thurgood Marshall .... page 16

Little Rock Nine .... page 17

Slow to Change .... page 18

Brown II and Beyond .... page 19

Get on the Bus, Gus! .... page 20

You Go Girls! .... page 21

English as a Second Language .... page 22

Education for All Handicapped Children Act .... page 23

Affirmative Action .... page 24

The Future .... page 25

Additional Resources .... page 26

Glossary .... page 27

Answer Key/Index .... page 28

Let's learn about
Brown v. Board of Education.

3

A Word From the Author

Dear Reader,

Brown v. Board of Education was a controversial Supreme Court decision in 1954. It was difficult for many people to understand and difficult for many people to deal with at that time. Today, there are still people who disagree with the Court's decision, but more importantly, the nation has moved away from segregation and closer to integration.

Yes, Brown v. Board of Education can be difficult to study. Many people stood up for what they believed so that future generations could benefit from their sacrifice.

The Supreme Court's decision in Brown v. Board of Education was more than just another Supreme Court decision, it was one of the first steps toward integration!

Since Brown v. Board of Education, many things in the United States have changed! The Court's decision brought an end to legal segregation and has made sure that all the nation's children are entitled to equal opportunities in education. Let's not forget all the good that has come since the Brown v. Board of Education decision (like any time period in history—those who don't learn from it are doomed to repeat it!).

Carole Marsh

A Timeline of Events

1868 – The Fourteenth Amendment guarantees "equal protection under the law"; citizenship is given to African Americans.

1896 – The *Supreme Court* authorizes segregation in *Plessy v. Ferguson*, ruling "separate but equal."

1938 – The *Supreme Court* rules the practice of sending black students out of state for legal training when the state provides a law school for whites within its borders does not fulfill the state's "separate but equal" obligation.

1948 – The *Supreme Court* orders the admission of a black student to the University of Oklahoma School of Law, a white school.

1950 – The *Supreme Court* rejects Texas' plan to create a new law school for black students rather than admit an African American to the state's whites-only law school.

1952 – The *Supreme Court* hears arguments in *Brown v. Board of Education*. Thurgood Marshall, who will later become the first African American justice on the Supreme Court, is the lead counsel for the parents of black school children.

1953 – The *Supreme Court* hears the second round of arguments in *Brown v. Board of Education*.

1954 – In a unanimous opinion issued on May 17, the Supreme Court in *Brown v. Board of Education* overturns *Plessy* and declares that separate schools are "inherently unequal." The Court delays deciding on how to implement the decision and asks for another round of arguments.

1955 – In *Brown II*, the Supreme Court orders the lower federal courts to require desegregation "with all deliberate speed."

5

I Want To Go To School!

Brown v. Board of Education

On May 17, 1954, Supreme Court Chief Justice Earl Warren read the Court's opinion in the case of *Brown v. Board of Education*. The Court, in a unanimous decision, decided that separate schools are "inherently unequal." The National Association for the Advancement of Colored People (NAACP) had their day in court—and they finally won! Much had been done for the cause of civil rights; still there was so much yet to do.

Integration did not take place overnight, but *Brown v. Board of Education* marked the point in time when the notion of equality moved away from just being an idea and took the first step toward becoming reality.

7

Equal Protection under the Law

Before the Civil War, many courts were divided on how to treat enslaved people. African Americans were often treated like property without any rights at all. But other times, enslaved people were treated like human beings. They were given a trial or made to appear in court as witnesses.

After the Civil War, the laws were changed to reflect a new way of life for former slaves. Many became landowners, voted, and even ran for office. The 13th, 14th, and 15th Amendments to the Constitution of the United States of America address the issue of slavery and guarantee equal protection under the law for all citizens.

- 13th Amendment: Bans slavery in the United States and any of its territories

- 14th Amendment: Grants citizenship to all persons born in the United States and guarantees them equal protection under the law

- 15th Amendment: Ensures all citizens the right to vote regardless of race or color or previous condition of servitude (formerly enslaved people)

Answer the following questions.

1. Which amendment banned slavery in the United States?

_____

2. Which amendment ensures all citizens the right to vote regardless of race?

_____

3. Which amendment grants citizenship to all persons born in the United States?

_____

4. How did life for slaves change after the Civil War?

_____

8

"Jim Crow" Laws

Jim Crow laws were a form of legal segregation. The laws made it legal to discriminate against African Americans in many communities and states. These laws took away equal opportunities in housing, work, education, and government mostly to African Americans, but for other minorities as well. African Americans were treated no better, and in a few cases, worse than in the days of slavery.

Jim Crow Laws required blacks and whites to have separate drinking fountains.

There were many African American leaders who spoke out against Jim Crow laws. They agreed that something should be done about them. However, they disagreed on what exactly should be done.

Booker T. Washington (1856–1915)
Washington stated he believed it was foolish for blacks to fight for civil rights before they had attained economic equality. He pleased many whites and gained financial support for his school, but many African American leaders disagreed with him.

W.E.B. Du Bois (1868–1963)
Du Bois was a co-founder of the Niagara Movement, which helped launch the National Association for the Advancement of Colored People (NAACP) in 1909. Du Bois demanded that African Americans achieve economic equality as well as full and immediate civil and political equality.

Marcus Garvey (1887–1940)
Marcus Garvey wanted to inspire all people of African ancestry to "redeem" Africa, and for European colonial powers to leave Africa. Garvey was born in Jamaica, but lived in New York City for a time.

Match the following leaders with their description.

1.
Booker T. Washington

2.
W.E.B. Du Bois

3.
Marcus Garvey

A. "I co-founded the Niagara Movement."

B. "I wanted colonial powers to leave Africa."

C. "Many African Americans disagreed with me, but I raised a lot of money for my school."

9

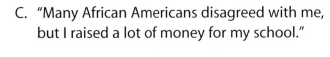

Separate but Equal

In 1890, the state of Louisiana passed a law called the "Separate Car Act." The law made it illegal for African Americans to ride in "white" railroad cars; instead they rode in "black" cars. A young man named Homer Plessy was put into jail for riding aboard a white car. He had refused to move to a black car.

Plessy and many others believed that the law violated the Fourteenth Amendment. In *Plessy v. Ferguson*, the Supreme Court said the Louisiana law did not violate the Fourteenth Amendment. The Supreme Court set a precedent with the "separate but equal" ruling, which prolonged an established system of discrimination against African Americans and other minorities.

Justice John Harlan was the only Supreme Court justice that thought "separate but equal" was a bad idea. He wrote, "Our Constitution is color-blind," and said that our country is not divided up into blacks and whites but that we are all equal. He was concerned that African Americans would not be treated equally—he was right.

Word Bank

color
equal
Harlan
Plessy
Supreme

Across

2. The _____ Court ruled "separate but equal" in the Plessy case.
5. John _____ was a Supreme Court Justice.

Down

1. Homer _____ refused to move to another railroad car.
3. We are all _____.
4. "Our Constitution is _____-blind."

10

Niagara Movement and the NAACP

The Niagara Movement was founded in Niagara Falls, Canada to fight racial discrimination in the United States. The Niagara Movement existed from 1905 to 1910. The movement failed to win the support of most African Americans, but many of its ideas were adopted in 1909 by a new interracial organization—the National Association for the Advancement of Colored People (NAACP).

The NAACP is the nation's oldest and largest civil rights organization. It works to end discrimination against blacks and other minority groups. The NAACP established the Spingarn Award as their highest honor in 1915. The award was named for Joel Elias Spingarn, who was then chairman of the NAACP's Board of Directors. This award recognizes great achievement by an African American.

Match these past Spingarn winners with their achievements.

_____ 1. Jackie Robinson

A. Actress and television personality

_____ 2. Martin Luther King, Jr.

B. First African American in modern major league baseball

_____ 3. Duke Ellington

C. Literature

_____ 4. Bill Cosby

D. Military

_____ 5. Colin L. Powell

E. Creative music

_____ 6. Maya Angelou

F. Civil rights

_____ 7. Oprah Winfrey

G. Entertainment; education

11

Attention Class

Before the Civil War, enslaved people were not allowed to read or write. It was illegal to teach black children, but many learned in secret. Even a few white slaveholders broke the law to teach their slaves so they could be of more use on the plantation.

A black teacher helping her students with their schoolwork.

Early black educators had to teach boys and girls how to succeed in a world that didn't want them to succeed. Education reformer Booker T. Washington was a world-renowned black educator at the Tuskegee Institute in the late 1800s. He thought white people would respect black people if more became educated.

Mary McLeod Bethune received an education funded by a kindly Quaker teacher. Bethune wanted other poor black children to have an opportunity to learn as she did. Starting with $1.50 in her pocket, Bethune founded Bethune-Cookman College in the early 1900s. She sold sweet potato pies and wrote letters to fund the school. Later, Bethune won a Spingarn Medal for her achievements.

Make each false statement true. Cross out the false word and write the correct word in the blank.

1. Booker T. Washington worked as a gardener. _____

2. Enslaved people were not allowed to read or sew. _____

3. Black slaveholders sometimes taught their slaves illegally. _____

4. Mary McLeod Bethune sold apple pies to fund her college. _____

5. Booker T. Washington taught at the Turtle Institute. _____

6. Teaching black children was allowed. _____

Booker T. Washington and Mary McLeod Bethune were both pioneers in African American education.

Building Blocks of *Brown*

There were many legal cases that came before the *Brown* case. In the 1930s Charles Hamilton Houston, an attorney for the NAACP, began challenging segregation in education through the courts. Here are some of the cases that helped clear the way for *Brown v. Board of Education*.

A. *Missouri ex rel. Gaines v. Canada* (1938)

The University of Missouri refused to admit Lloyd Gaines to its law school because it believed the school was only for whites. The U.S. Supreme Court ruled Gaines must be allowed to attend the University of Missouri's Columbia School of Law.

B. *Sipuel v. Board of Regents of the University of Oklahoma* (1948)

When Ada Lois Sipuel was denied entry to law school, the University set up a school overnight with 3 instructors, 3 classrooms, and separate access to the law library at the state capital. The U.S. Supreme Court ruled this was illegal, and Sipuel was finally allowed to enroll in the law school of the University of Oklahoma.

C. *McLaurin v. Oklahoma State Regents for Higher Education* (1950)

The U.S. Supreme Court ruled that George W. McLaurin, a black student who was required to eat and study at separate tables, must be treated the same as white students. Chief Justice Fred Vinson said in the ruling that "McLaurin must receive the same treatment... as students of other races."

D. *Sweatt v. Painter* (1950)

This case was most important to *Brown v. Board of Education*, because the U.S. Supreme Court decided 9-0 that the "separate but equal" policy established in the *Plessy* case was not realistic and eventually would be overruled.

Match the description with each case from above. Write the letter for the correct case in the space provided.

_____ 1. Supreme Court decided that "separate but equal" was wrong.

_____ 2. Set up a "class" overnight with 3 instructors.

_____ 3. Justice Vinson stated that a student "must receive the same treatment... as other races."

_____ 4. Supreme Court ruled that an African American student must be allowed to attend the University of Missouri-Columbia School of Law.

13

Segregation

Teaching a lesson in a segregated school.

Imagine what life was like for children during segregation. Schools were segregated and so was everything else! African Americans and whites were taught at an early age to know the difference between the signs that read "white" and "colored." Signs marked drinking fountains, entrances to buildings, and schools.

Brown v. Board of Education is best remembered as a legal victory in the fight to end the unequal and unfair practice of segregation. But African American parents began to challenge racial segregation in public education as early as 1849 in the case of *Roberts v. City of Boston, Massachusetts*. From 1881 to 1949, Kansas was the site of eleven similar cases.

What made Brown different from earlier cases? The NAACP decided to take their concerns about segregated schools to the Federal courts. In the past, only state courts had ruled in these cases. Local NAACP Chapters in Delaware, Kansas, South Carolina, Virginia, and Washington D.C. recruited parents to be plaintiffs.

Brown v. Board of Education was about the entire African American population who had grown tired of injustice. The NAACP believed that settling differences in court was the best solution to a nationwide problem.

Write About It!

How does it feel to be "outnumbered"? Maybe there are fewer boys in your class, or fewer girls. Maybe you've been the only one with glasses, freckles, curly hair, or the only one who forgot to bring their permission slip to go on a field trip.

Write about a time when you were "outnumbered."
How did it make you feel?

_____

_____

_____

_____

Who Was Brown?

Brown v. Board of Education of Topeka was a case decided in 1954 in which the Supreme Court of the United States declared racial segregation in public schools to be unconstitutional. The full name of the case is *Brown et al v. Board of Education of Topeka et al.* The Topeka case lists Oliver Brown and twelve other families whose parents took a stand against segregation as a group.

Rev. Oliver Brown

The Topeka, Kansas case was first presented in 1951 before the Federal District Court, but the parents and families lost. *Brown* was then appealed to the Supreme Court of the United States. The Court decided the case together with several others that dealt with the same issue. The Court applied its decision to all of the cases at the same time. The separate cases were from four different states and the District of Columbia. All total the five cases under the heading of *Brown* represented more than 200 plaintiffs and twelve different attorneys and community activists. The five cases were from:

- Delaware — *Belton (Bulah) v. Gebhart*
- Kansas — *Brown v. Board of Education of Topeka*
- South Carolina — *Briggs v. Elliot*
- Virginia — *Davis v. County School Board of Prince Edward County*
- Washington, DC — *Bolling v. Sharpe*

Color the places where each of the cases took place.

Thurgood Marshall

The National Association for the Advancement of Colored People (NAACP), guided by its chief lawyer, Thurgood Marshall, decided to use *Brown* and its companion cases to challenge the "separate but equal" principle. The Supreme Court ruled against segregation in public schools. The Court held that "in the field of public education the doctrine of 'separate but equal' has no place. Separate educational facilities are inherently unequal." The Court cited evidence that African American children were adversely affected by segregation.

Thurgood Marshall

Thurgood Marshall studied law at Howard University and began practicing law in 1933. From 1938 to 1950, Marshall served as chief counsel for the NAACP. From 1940 to 1961, he was director and chief counsel for the NAACP Legal Defense and Educational Fund.

Marshall was awarded the Spingarn Medal in 1946. In 1961, Marshall was appointed to the U.S. Court of Appeals. In 1965, he was appointed solicitor general of the United States. President Lyndon B. Johnson appointed Marshall the first African American justice of the Supreme Court of the United States. He served as an associate justice from 1967 until his retirement in 1991.

Leading the way!

Charles Hamilton Houston served as an officer during World War I before attending Harvard Law School. He was the Dean of Howard University Law School while Thurgood Marshall studied there. Later, Houston became a special counsel for the NAACP and argued important civil rights cases before the Supreme Court. Houston was an inspiration to Marshall and many other civil rights leaders.

Put the events in Thurgood Marshall's life in the correct order.

_____ 1. Awarded the Spingarn Medal

_____ 2. Marshall was appointed to the U.S. Court of Appeals

_____ 3. Retired from the Supreme Court

_____ 4. Appointed solicitor general of the United States

_____ 5. Began practicing law

_____ 6. Began serving as director and chief counsel for the NAACP Legal Defense and Educational Fund

_____ 7. Was appointed to the Supreme Court by President Lyndon B. Johnson

_____ 8. Presented the legal argument ending racial segregation in public schools

_____ 9. Began service as chief counsel for the NAACP

_____ 10. Ended service as chief counsel for the NAACP

A. 1946

B. 1933

C. 1965

D. 1950

E. 1991

F. 1961

G. 1967

H. 1938

I. 1940

J. 1954

16

Little Rock Nine

President Dwight Eisenhower favored an orderly end to racial discrimination against African Americans. But in September 1957 a crisis in Little Rock, Arkansas, became one of the most famous cases of integration—Little Rock Nine!

Governor Orval E. Faubus blocked nine black students from entering Central High in Little Rock because he didn't want to integrate Little Rock's schools. The governor used the Arkansas National Guard to prevent black students from entering the school. President Eisenhower sent federal troops to protect the nine black students. President Eisenhower then sent a regular Army unit, the 101st Airborne Division, to enforce the court order and protect the black students. In a television appearance, Eisenhower explained that he wanted to prevent further civil disorder.

From left, standing, are Ernest Green, Melba Pattillo, Jefferson Thomas, Carlotta Walls, and Terrance Roberts (next to Daisy Bates, president of the Arkansas Chapter of the NAACP). From left, seated, are Thelma Mothershed, Minnie Jean Brown, Elizabeth Eckford, and Gloria Ray.

News Flash!

You are reporting for the Central High School Newspaper, *The Tiger*, and you have set up several interviews. How do you think the following people will feel about the Little Rock Nine? **Write your answers below.**

1. Governor Faubus _____

_____

2. President Eisenhower _____

_____

3. Soldier in the Arkansas National Guard _____

_____

4. Soldier in the 101st Airborne Division _____

_____

5. One of the "Little Rock Nine" _____

_____

6. Teacher at Central High School _____

_____

17

Slow to Change

In 1954, the Supreme Court of the United States agreed that segregation in public schools was wrong. The Court said, "in the field of public education the doctrine of 'separate but equal' has no place. Separate educational facilities are inherently unequal." What that meant was that being separate could not possibly be equal, so segregation was wrong.

By 1960, however, several Southern states still had no black students enrolled in public schools with white students. Some progress was made in these states later in the 1960s, after civil rights protests and new federal laws desegregated other public places. Many courts used ideas established in the *Brown* case to require the desegregation of public facilities.

In *Davis v. County School Board of Prince Edward County Virginia*, a case that was part of the *Brown* decision, the school system refused to integrate. The Board of Supervisors for Prince Edward County would not give money to the County School Board from 1959 until 1964. They closed the schools rather than integrate them. White students began attending all-white private schools. Black students were forced to go to school elsewhere or give up their education altogether. Prince Edward County Schools reopened in 1965 with another Supreme Court order.

Do the Math!

1. How many years were Prince Edward County Public Schools closed?

Year reopened	**1964**
Year closed	**— 1959**
Answer:	

2. How many years passed between the *Brown* decision and the reopening of Prince Edward County Public Schools?

Year reopened	**1964**
Brown decision	**— 1954**
Answer:	

3. How many years has it been since the Supreme Court ruled in the *Brown* case?

Current Year	_ _ _ _
Brown decision	**— 1954**
Answer:	

Now it's starting to add up!

18

Brown II and Beyond

Even though the Supreme Court had ruled against segregation in 1954, the Court did not give any deadline for desegregation. The Court asked to hear another round of arguments in 1955 to decide how the schools should be integrated. In *Brown II*, the Supreme Court ordered schools to integrate "with all deliberate speed." This wording would haunt the victims of segregation for many years. The intent of the Court was to move forward with integration. However, the segregated schools used the unclear wording of the decision as an excuse to delay integration.

The United States Supreme Court is the highest court in the land.

The struggle for integration was long and difficult. Between 1955 and 1960, federal judges held more than 200 school desegregation hearings. Across the nation, people protested as the first wave of African American students began to enroll in and attend desegregated public schools and universities. In many cases, there were riots, and the National Guard was called out to protect students (some as young as six years old!) from violent protesters.

Throughout the 1960s, many legal victories were won in the cause for desegregation. The Civil Rights Act of 1964 was adopted. The Act prohibits discrimination in programs and activities including schools that receive federal money. Finally in 1969, the Supreme Court ordered public school districts to desegregate "at once."

Solve the code.

A B C D E F G H I J K L M N O P Q R S T U V W X Y Z

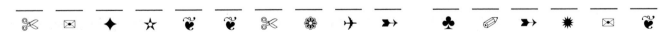

Six-year-old Ruby Bridges was guarded by federal marshals when she attempted to enroll for school in New Orleans, Louisiana in 1960.

Get on the Bus, Gus!

In the 1970s, opportunities for African American students to be educated in desegregated schools increased as the Supreme Court allowed busing to integrate public schools. The Supreme Court often ordered the busing of students to make sure that most schools would have a similar number of minority students. Busing and other desegregation efforts have caused much controversy since the 1970s.

Busing students begins with the boundary line of a school district. Officials try to decide where to send students based on race. The idea was that instead of having segregated schools, each school would have the same minority population.

Some felt that busing was the only way for integration to work since neighborhoods were segregated and most students went to schools in their neighborhood. Students often rode buses for very long distances in order to attend a newly integrated school.

Others felt that busing was not the right solution for desegregation. They believed that it was unfair for students to ride long distances no matter what the school was like. Some feel that more effort should be made to improve or build a school that is closer to home than to send students great distances.

Questions for Discussion

1. If you had to choose between riding a bus for long distances so that you could attend a better school, or attending a school that was close to home but was of lesser quality, which would you choose?

   _____

   _____

2. How would it make you feel if you were forced to ride the bus a long distance to school everyday even though there was a very good school in your own neighborhood?

   _____

   _____

20

You Go Girls!

The idea of equal opportunity for all races eventually spread to equal opportunity for both boys and girls. Beginning in 1972, girls in public schools receiving federal funds began receiving the same educational opportunities as boys in all aspects of schooling, including math, science, athletics, and other school programs. This was called Title IX and was part of the Education Amendments of 1972.

United States Representative Edith Green introduced a higher education bill with provisions regarding discrimination against girls. It took a House-Senate Conference Committee several months to settle on the more than 250 differences between the House and Senate education bills. The final legislation became Title IX.

Title IX of the Education Amendments of 1972 bans discrimination on the basis of sex by schools and colleges receiving federal funds. This law applies to discrimination in all areas of school activity, including admissions, athletics, and educational programs.

Write a headline story about an all-girl sports team.

Be sure to answer the Who? What? Where? When? Why? and How?

Go Get 'em Girls!

 Virginia state law once prohibited women from being admitted to the College of Arts and Sciences of the University of Virginia. It was only under court order in 1970 that the first woman was admitted!

21

English as a Second Language

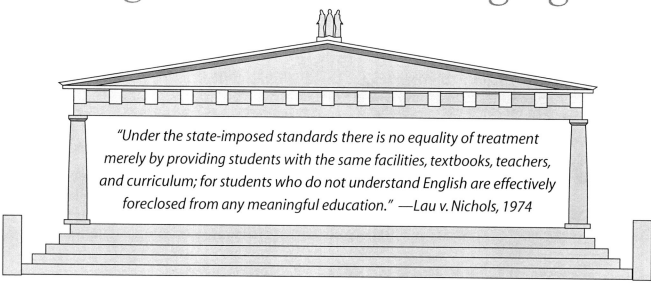

"Under the state-imposed standards there is no equality of treatment merely by providing students with the same facilities, textbooks, teachers, and curriculum; for students who do not understand English are effectively foreclosed from any meaningful education." —Lau v. Nichols, 1974

This Supreme Court ruling that the San Francisco school system violated the Civil Rights Act of 1964 by not providing English language instruction to approximately 1,800 Chinese American students led to the spread of bilingual education in the United States.

Before the 1960s, if students in the United States did not speak English, they had a very difficult time getting an education. If students were lucky, there might be a private school or a private tutor who could teach them how to speak English. Although many schools taught foreign languages, very few schools taught any other subjects in anything but English.

The Bilingual Education Acts of 1968 and 1974, provided money for school districts interested in establishing programs to meet the "special educational needs" of large numbers of children of limited English speaking ability in the United States.

Think About It

Imagine what life in the United States must be like for a student who cannot read or write any English. It would be more than difficult; it would be nearly impossible without some help.

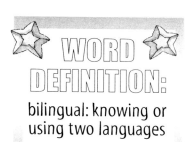

WORD DEFINITION:
bilingual: knowing or using two languages

What is the official language of the United States of America?

The U.S. does not have one.

22

Education for All Handicapped Children Act

On November 19, 1975, The Education for All Handicapped Children Act of 1975 was enacted into law. The original legislation was introduced in May 1972, after several landmark court cases established the right to education for all handicapped children.

The Supreme Court said, "In these days, it is doubtful that any child may reasonably be expected to succeed in life if he is denied the opportunity of an education. Such an opportunity... is a right which must be made available to all on equal terms." Since 1975, the law has been changed and renamed several times. On June 4, 1997, the Individuals with Disabilities Education Act was changed again. The new version of the law is often called "IDEA 97."

The "idea" of this law is that all physically challenged students are entitled to a fair and appropriate public education. Students must have access to specialized materials and equipment if necessary, such as Braille books for blind students.

Most students who cannot hear use sign language to communicate with their teachers, other students, and their families.

Study the sign language alphabet below. Then practice "signing" your name.

This must be a good sign!

23

Affirmative Action

Lyndon B. Johnson

In 1964, President Lyndon B. Johnson issued two executive orders. They required government contractors and schools that received federal money to develop affirmative action programs. Affirmative action is any policy or program designed to end discrimination against minorities and women (especially in employment and education).

The idea was that certain groups (especially women and minority groups) would be given special treatment when being considered for jobs, college admission, and other social benefits. Because there were no or few women and minorities in positions of power, many felt this was necessary in order to give all people certain opportunities.

In the 1970s, some argued that affirmative action created "reverse discrimination." Some people felt that it was unfair for minorities and women to be given special consideration for jobs and other opportunities.

Arguments over affirmative action continue today. The Civil Rights Act of 1991 reaffirmed the federal government's commitment to affirmative action. However, in the late 1990s, California and other states banned the use of affirmative action in state and local programs. But in 2003, a U.S. Supreme Court decision reaffirmed affirmative action in a case regarding college admission. They said it was OK to give special treatment to minorities in some cases.

Integration Interview

Find an adult you can interview about the desegregation/integration of schools then ask these questions. Record his or her answers below.

1. Which event of integration do you remember most?

_____

2. How has integration affected you and/or your family?

_____

3. What did you do to help the process of integration move smoothly?

_____

24

The Future

The nation marked the 50th anniversary of *Brown v. Board of Education* in 2004. As time passes, people have recognized the many benefits of having desegregated classrooms. These include:

- Reducing stereotypes and prejudices

- Offering students opportunities for learning how to function in integrated environments

- Promoting cross-racial understanding that brings out different viewpoints, skills, and values that will enhance students' abilities to succeed

Question for Discussion

Read the following statements, then decide whether they are an advantage or a disadvantage of integration. Write advantage or disadvantage in the space provided.

_____ 1. Integration of schools led to integration of many other parts of society.

_____ 2. Some students were threatened because they decided to attend an integrated school.

_____ 3. All students were given the opportunity for an equal education.

_____ 4. Students can speak and learn from other students with different cultural backgrounds.

Where Are We Today?

In 2003, a study by Harvard's Civil Rights Project found that schools were more segregated in 2000 than in 1970 when busing for desegregation began. Why is this so? There are no more laws that force people to attend segregated schools. Instead, people just seem to move to areas where there are more people like themselves creating a kind of cultural segregation.

25

Additional Resources

BOOKS

Separate but Not Equal: The Dream and the Struggle by James Haskins, ©2002. Published by Polaris.

Rosa Parks: My Story by Rosa Parks, James Haskins, ©1999. Published by Puffin Books

Rosetta, Rosetta, Sit by Me! by Linda Walvoord, Eric Velasquez, ©2004. Published by Marshall Cavendish Children's Books.

Brown V. Board of Education: Equal Schooling for All (Landmark Supreme Court Cases) by Harvey Fireside, Sarah Betsy Fuller, ©1994. Published by Enslow Publishers.

Through My Eyes by Ruby Bridges, Margo Lundell, ©1999. Published by Scholastic.

WEBSITES

http://brownvboard.org/
http://ktwu.washburn.edu/productions/brownvboard/
http://www.nps.gov/brvb/

http://brownvboard.org/brownquarterly/
Contains links to previous editions of the Brown Quarterly

PLAY

Now Let Me Fly by Marcia Cebulska, http://anationacts.brownvboard.org

VIDEOS

Black, White, & Brown: Brown versus the Board of Education of Topeka
The Road to Brown
Reading, Writing and Resistance
In Pursuit of Freedom and Equality: The Story of Brown v. Board of Education of Topeka

Glossary

abolitionist: one who works against slavery; someone who does not agree with slavery; a person who opposes slavery; a person who fought to end slavery

amendment: a correction or change made to a document such as the U.S. Constitution; a change in, or addition to, a constitution, law, or bill

boycott: to join with others and refuse to buy, sell, or use something; refusing to buy a product to show disapproval of a company

civil rights: the rights of all citizens regardless of race, gender, or religion

constitution: the system of basic laws or rules of a government

de facto segregation: segregation of racial or other groups resulting from circumstances, such as housing patterns, rather than from official policy or law

de jure segregation: racial segregation that is a direct result of law or official policy.

emancipation: set free from slavery or strict control

integration: becoming an accepted member of a group or a community

minorities: a small group of people of a different race or religion

movement: the actions of a group of people to bring about change

precedent: a law established by following earlier judicial decisions

proclamation: an official public statement

segregation: To separate based on race

social reform: change

Answer Key

Page 8   1. 13th; 2. 15th; 3. 14th; 4. Former slaves became landowners, began to vote, and ran for office

Page 9   1.C; 2.A; 3.B

Page 10   1. Plessy rode the "white" railroad car; 2. "Separate but equal"; 3. Justice John Harlan

Page 11   1.B; 2.F; 3.E; 4.G; 5.D; 6.C; 7.A

Page 12   1. educator; 2. write; 3. white; 4. sweet potato; 5. Tuskegee; 6. illegal

Page 13   1.D; 2.B; 3.C; 4.A

Page 16   1.A; 2.F; 3.E; 4.C; 5.B; 6.I; 7.G; 8.J; 9.H; 10.D

Page 17   Answers may vary

Page 18   1. 5 years; 2. 10 years; 3. Answers will vary

Page 20   Answers will vary

Page 21   Answers will vary

Page 24   Answers will vary

Page 25   Answers will vary

Index

Affirmative Action **24**

Bethune, Mary McLeod **12**

Bilingual Education Act **22**

Bridges, Ruby **19**

Brown v. Board of Education **15, 18**

Brown, Oliver **15**

busing **20, 25**

Du Bois, W.E.B. **9**

Eisenhower, Dwight **17**

Fifteenth Amendment **8**

Fourteenth Amendment **8**

Garvey, Marcus **9**

Harlan, John **10**

Houston, Charles H. **16**

Individuals with Disabilities Education Act **23**

Johnson, Lyndon **16, 24**

Little Rock Nine **17**

Marshall, Thurgood **16**

NAACP **11, 13, 14, 16**

Niagara Movement **11**

Plessy v. Ferguson **10**

segregation **14, 18, 25**

Spingarn Medal **16**

Thirteenth Amendment **8**

Title IX **21**

Washington, Booker T. **9, 12**